Penelope

by

thelwell

NEW YORK
E. P. DUTTON & CO., INC.
1973

First published in the U.S.A. 1973 by E. P. Dutton & Co., Inc.
Copyright © 1972 by Norman Thelwell and Beaverbrook Newspapers Ltd.
All rights reserved. Printed in the U.S.A.

FIRST EDITION

SBN: 0-525-17722-1
Library of Congress Catalog Card Number: 72-94690

" I DON'T THINK MUCH OF HIS SEAT. "

This book is based on a series which appeared
in the Sunday Express

" I'LL BE GLAD WHEN SHE GETS INTERESTED IN BOYS. "

" COME ALONG GIRLS . PLAY TIME'S OVER "

"WHAT A SHAME! THERE GOES HER EGG AND SPOON."

48

" SHE'S NOT MAKING VERY RAPID PROGRESS, I'M AFRAID "

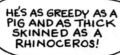

71

" SHE LOVES THAT PONY - NEVER OUT OF THE SADDLE. "

73

74

I'M WORRIED ABOUT KIPPER, FIONA. HE'S GOT A TOUCH OF INSOMNIA!

I'M SURE I'M RIGHT BUT I'D APPRECIATE A SECOND OPINION

THERE! DID YOU SEE THAT EYELID FLICKER?

I'M BEGINNING TO UNDERSTAND WHY SOME PEOPLE WORSHIP THEIR ANCESTORS!

" HURRY UP!   I'M ON HORSEBACK . "

EVERY DAY THE NEWSPAPERS ARE FULL OF SUCH HORRIBLE THINGS, IT MAKES ME WORRY ABOUT WHAT'S GOING TO BECOME OF US ALL!

THERE'S NO SENSE IN WORRYING ABOUT THE FUTURE, FIONA!

YOU'VE GOT TO LEARN HOW TO ENJOY **TODAY**!